With My Mom and Dad

Written by Margie Burton, Cathy French, and Tammy Jones

I go to the bank
with my dad.

In one action –
insert your card a
take it right out.

3

Mom and I go
to the pond.

I go to the doctor
with my mom.

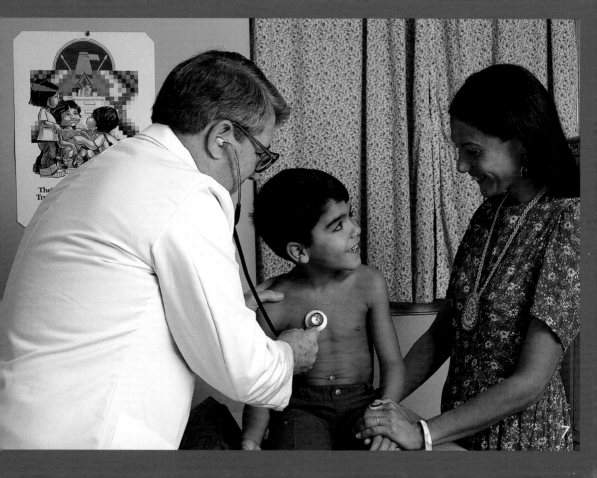

I go to the store
with my dad.

I go to the park with my dad to play.

Dad and I go
to the mailbox.

I go to the library
with my mom.

We go home
to read the books.